GOBLIN IN THE FRIDGE

POEMS BY

MATT BLACK

Illustrated by

Cathy Benson

Chess Black

Matt Black

Michael Black

Tiffany Black

Leora Brook

Bob Pomfret

Jackie Prachek

Keith Turner

Upside Down Books

Matt Black was born in 1956 in Oxford. He caught a bus to Sheffield in 1985 and has been living there ever since. His kitchen has had cereal boxes all over the walls for the last 15 years and he has 2 children who are pretty much grown up now.

Since 1991 he has been writing poems and performing his poetry. He has set a World Record (unofficial) performing in 50 venues in 5 hours on a tandem, and works regularly at festivals and schools with his Poetry Jukebox. He has won awards and commissions and has toured in Germany, U.S.A., Ireland, Poland and the Czech Republic. He enjoys working with artists and musicians.

As a young lad Matt wanted to play football for England or play tennis at Wimbledon. However, he has always loved reading and writing and that's why he has made this book of poems. He's had lots of daft jobs - shoe-shine boy, farmer, builder, office boy, gardener, but this being a poet lark is the most enjoyable and interesting by a long way and so he's sticking with that for now. He has an old-fashioned rickety-rackety caravan and likes gooseberry crumble.

Cathy Benson illustrates words, writes about the pictures in her head and shares her work with people of all ages. She loves cats, the sea, the beach and vanilla ice cream.

Chess Black trained as an art teacher, became a sound engineer, then painted theatre scenery, and now earns a living as a part-time eLearning consultant and paints.

Michael Black one? two? me? cor! live* kiss! heaven!! eight? fine – again. Devon! dozing – flirteen, naughteen, lifteen, fixteen, umpteen, dateen, mineteen, plenty.

Leora Brook and **Tiffany Black** work together in print, film, sound and sculpture as brook and black, making installations and artworks which respond to various sites and situations in Britain and abroad (www.brookandblack.co.uk).

Bob Pomfret has been drawing cartoons since he was at school a thousand years ago. When not drawing he likes to run up and down hills or watch Oxford United.

Jackie Prachek has worked as a cartoonist, illustrator and community artist since 1980. Her work has been published and exhibited in Europe and America and she has represented England at the World Comics Convention in Angoulême, France.

Keith Turner works as a graphic designer and set up design agency 'mooli' with Damian Witty in 2002. Since then he has drawn unicorns, dinosaurs, aliens, trees, birds and air conditioning units. He enjoys drawing some things more than others.

THIS BOOK BELONGS TO

Name ~~Jacob~~ Jacob

Age 6

Height tall

Favourite Word So

Likes... football

Dislikes... M Night Mare's

Favourite form of transport train

Favourite biscuit Ginger flaver

Animal Spirit
(what animal is your spirit most like?) Cheaters

"...Well, now that we *have* seen each other,"
said the Unicorn,

"if you'll believe in me,
I'll believe in you."

Through the Looking Glass **Lewis Carroll**

For Max, Saul, Jessie, Georgia, Paris, Lily, Dulcie, Ralphie and Jo
With love Matt

With thanks to Gerard Benson for editorial advice, and to Arts Council England
(Yorkshire) for financial support.

Some of these poems have been published in The Poetry Store (Hodder and
Stoughton), The Universal Vacuum Cleaner and other riddle poems (Oxford
University Press), Silly Poems (Scholastic), How to Survive School (Macmillan) and
Scary Poems to Make You Shiver (Oxford University Press).

Published in 2007 by
Upside Down Books
51 Pearson Place
Sheffield S8 9DE
www.matt-black.co.uk/upsidedownbooks

ISBN 978-0-9516766-6-0

A CIP catalogue record for this book is available from the British Library.

Typeset and design
Mooli
Mountfields House, Epinal Way
Loughborough LE11 3GE
www.mooli.com

Printed by Lighthouse Colour Limited,
3 Charnwood Business Park, North Rd,
Loughborough LE11 1LE
www.lighthouse-colour.co.uk

Contents

FROM WORDS TO POEMS

Find your way from WORDS to POEMS in just four moves, changing one letter at a time and making a new word each time.

WORDS

Words
----

poems
----

poems
----

poms

POEMS

Alphabetti Spaghetti

It changed the day when he opened a tin of alphabet spaghetti
He poured the pasta letters in a bowl in patterns that looked pretty
In pink tomato sauce he looked for cool words like **ELECTRICITY**
It helped him with his spellings and fed his deeper sense of mystery

He made up stuff like **HWAA** and grew his very own vocabulary
POGGLE, WIBBLIES, DOODAH - which was actually in the dictionary
Sorting out the letters made life feel less jittery and slippery
Even when he spelt stuff rong like **JOOSE** and **JOGRAFEE** and **HISTREE**

MOON made him moony but in a good way while **SUNSHINE** made him sunny
And hungry for words he found the pasta letters soon filled his tummy
Sometimes it was just for fun, they said, and sometimes he made poetry
But he always liked the games he played in the alphabet spaghetti

Snap Crackle Pop

Good morning
says the warm blanket over my head
Good morning
says the juice by the side of my bed
Good morning
says a voice, five to eight
Okay, Mum, good timing,
I say, I'm going to be late

Good morning
say my pants going up my legs
Good morning
says the smell of fried eggs
Good morning
say my feet scuttling down stairs
Good morning
says the kitchen table to the chairs

Good morning
says the orange box pouring its juice
Good morning
says the radio speaking the news
Good morning
says my Mum, just look at the clock
Good morning
say the rice crispies, and snap crackle pop

Good morning
say the front door and the wheelie-bins
Good morning
says my friend Jack, and the day begins

Biro Clutcher

Paper scratcher
Sky watcher

Word gatherer
Story speaker

Dream weaver
Idea stealer

Music maker
Heart shaker

Serious thinker
Daft joker

Tea drinker
Thought provoker

Rhyme cruncher
Sandwich muncher

QUICK PRIZE QUIZ

1. The poem above is a riddle. What or who is it about?
2. In most countries the first poets started by making up oral poetry. What is oral poetry?
3. In India and Pakistan at poetry readings ('mushaira' in Urdu) poets often repeat lines and audiences ask for lines to be said again. If a listener likes something, they generally say Wah! Wah! (in Urdu and Hindi) or Bah! Bah! in Bengali. Listeners also repeat favourite lines with the poet. Do you like this idea? Why?
4. In Japan they have lots of different words for different kinds of rain, and they also write lots of poems about rain. What is the name of the very short kind of poem (with 17 syllables) which Japanese poets are famous for writing?
5. What is the shortest poem in the world?
6. What is your favourite poem? Why?
7. What do poets put in their sandwiches?

Answers to quizzes@matt-black.co.uk

Send us 7 good answers (not all the questions have right answers, we just like good answers) and we'll send you a new, still steaming, freshly cooked poem.

9

Sky's Daughter

If you walk into mist a story begins
If you eat snow snowmen appear in your dreams
If you see a whale in a pond it's time to wake up
Falling in streams brings you good luck
 These are the laws of water, sky's daughter

If you watch a river too long you start to feel old
One cup of water is worth two buckets of gold
If you look at clouds long enough a dragon appears
Icicles don't grow on my grandfather's beard
 These are the laws of water, sky's daughter

If you watch the wild sea you start to grow wise
If you leave a tap running a cactus plant cries
At the centre of whirlpools devils make plans
Goblins hide in watering-cans
 These are the laws of water, sky's daughter

If you stand in puddles it will help you grow tall
If you watch the tides turn you sometimes feel small
Sleeping lakes dream of fish falling through air
Waterfalls are rivers washing their hair
 These are the laws of water, sky's daughter

Air Music

I sleep in your chest like the gentlest of lions
I flow through your hair like a river of tongues
Your first and last breath, your feast and your friend
I love you at birth, set you free at the end
Invisible, everywhere
I am air

I am the string that pulls clouds through the sky
I am the beat when swans start to fly
I whip up the waves and the white water
I dance on street corners with pieces of paper
Invisible, everywhere
I am air

I flutter my eyelids where hummingbirds hover
I blow the warm breeze that smiles through summer
I am the cold shadow that ripples the corn
I am the terror of trees in a storm
Invisible, everywhere
I am air

I rise in balloons up to the Sun
I howl through werewolves under the Moon
I am the genie where the whirlwind swirls
I rustle the leaves at the end of the world
Invisible, everywhere
Invincible, air

The Big Life Incubator Blanket

leaf-turf rain-filter
rabbit-run sun-soaker -
where the soft hills turn

loam-home stone-catcher
root-crop potato-grower -
where the black dog scratches

mole-town crumble-heaper
compost-heaven rose-feeder -
where the orange mud squelches

soil-music seed-storer
night-cave water-bringer -
where the big bull roars

creepy-crawly tunnel-holder
worm-city ant-tickler –
where the tired donkey dreams

moo-breath mist-floor
volcano-heart melt-core
where the earth burns

Where the Wild Wind

I am
a turning bubble but a million times bigger,
a mystery of mountains and valleys and water,

I am
hanging in the sky with the moon and the weather,
watching the stars and space stretching forever,

I am
your backyard, your garden, your future,
your promise, your playground, your treasure,

I am
where the wild wind rushes over,
yours to live on, yours to look after

Lord of the Doughnuts
(for Homer Simpson, Doh!)

Magic melting mouthful maker,
Sweet-tooth secret truth of grown-ups,
Ruler of all Squidginess,
Lord of the Doughnuts,

Older than Gandalf the Grey,
And before the round world ever began,
No stars twinkling, just his small voice singing
Lord of the Doughnuts, I am

Shaping with flour the first sugary sun
Out of the darkness, and watching it rise,
Till the glittering crown, golden brown,
Glowed in the kitchen in the skies

COLOUR IN THESE PAGES
AS YOU LIKE...

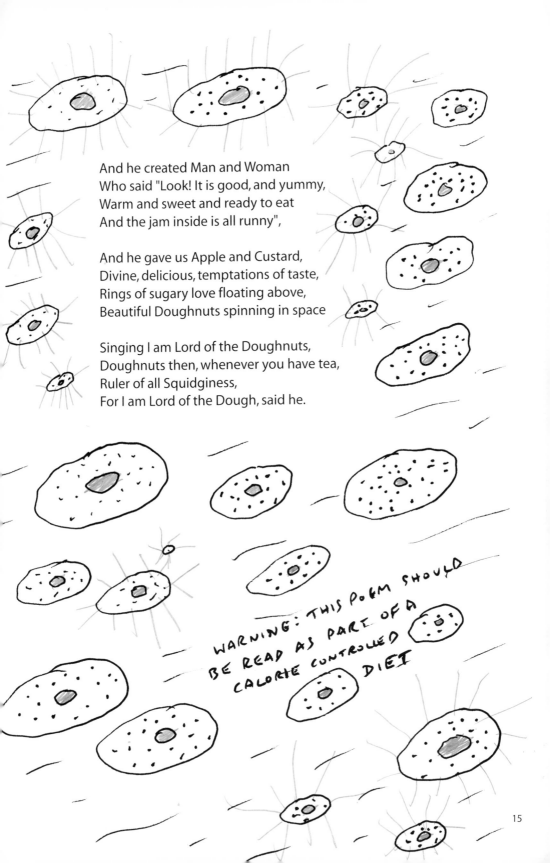

And he created Man and Woman
Who said "Look! It is good, and yummy,
Warm and sweet and ready to eat
And the jam inside is all runny",

And he gave us Apple and Custard,
Divine, delicious, temptations of taste,
Rings of sugary love floating above,
Beautiful Doughnuts spinning in space

Singing I am Lord of the Doughnuts,
Doughnuts then, whenever you have tea,
Ruler of all Squidginess,
For I am Lord of the Dough, said he.

WARNING: THIS POEM SHOULD BE READ AS PART OF A CALORIE CONTROLLED DIET

Wriggly Riddly

I am Wobbly and Wibbly
and Shivery and Shakey

Slippey and Slidey
on Spoony and Platey

Pinky or Purpley,
Yellowy, Greeny

Tea-time or Party,
covered in Creamy

Trifley and Fruity
and Floppy and Yummy

I squiggle and wriggle
when I'm in your Tummy -

so tell me, oh tell me
what do you call me?

Jelly

Answer at back of book

Pizza Pizza

O pizza pizza margherita,
My favourite, my fiery wheel,
O piece of pizza, can I eat yer,
Can I have you every meal?

Squelchy, spicy, chewy ring
Of tomato, cheese and creamy dough,
Golden honey-crusted heaven,
Warm sea of goo - I love you so!

Your glowing red and yellow sun
Melting, and I lick my lips
As you slide over the moon of my plate
Making a total eclipse!

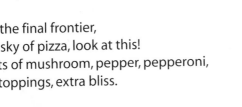

So feast of pizza, peace of pizza,
Nothing beats yer inner glow,
When I meet yer, I must eat yer,
The thrill, the frill, the hill of dough.

Taste, the final frontier,
In my sky of pizza, look at this!
Planets of mushroom, pepper, pepperoni,
Extra toppings, extra bliss.

O pizza pizza margherita,
How I wonder what's for tea,
O stuffed crust in the sky above
I hope you're big enough for me.

HILL OF DOH!

To find out more about pizzas — see inside back
cover. To make own pizza, very easy, take flour,
water, make dough (or buy ready made dough or base,
even easier), cover with favourite toppings, put in
oven, savour the flavour etcetera

dot-2-dot

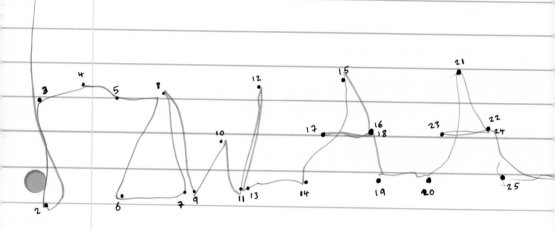

call my bluff

Here are 3 possible meanings for

DOODAH   3

Guess which meaning
is the right one.

1. A nickname or term of fondness for a father.

2. A flutter of excitement.

3. A small old-fashioned trumpet. ✓

Make up a new meaning for DOODAH.
Send it to *quizzes@matt-black.co.uk* and if we
think it is good we will send you a sparkling,
shining, newly polished poem.

Neither of these words are in the dictionary.

POGGLE   WIBBLIES

Make up a meaning for each of them and
send it to quizzes@matt-black.co.uk and
if we think they are good we will send
you a scary old poem covered in spiders
and cobwebs.

18

HOUSE QUIZ

Every person has their own word hoard, which is the special collection of words which only that person uses. Nobody has exactly the same set of words as anyone else.

Every house has its own word hoard.

WRITE YOUR ANSWERS HERE OR JUST CHAT ABOUT THEM WITH SOMEONE ELSE IN YOUR HOUSE

What is the most commonly used word in your house?

nah

What is the most commonly used phrase in your house?

that'll do

For each person in your house think of a phrase that they often use.

whatever

What is your favourite long word?

to transparent

What is your favourite word that you don't understand?

comprehised

Who does the washing up?

dad

Why?

mums
prengnent

Tigers

Tonight Mum and Dad
are snarling at each other,
like two angry tigers
prowling round the kitchen.

Is it me
they're fighting over?
What have I done wrong?
Have I upset them?

They think I can't hear.
But my ears are sharp,
pricked like a young cub
up here, alone in my bedroom.

They don't tell me what's wrong.
But I can see life is not always easy
and I'm growing stronger and wiser
as I watch them.

Foolish old tigers.
I know it's tough.
But if they came up here
I'd purr and I'd lick them.

Split

They split
like a single tree ripped in two
by zig-zags of lightning,
frightening.

Mum took all our bedroom things,
toothbrushes, towels, flannels
and all the kitchen stuff.
She said she'd had enough.

I stayed at Dad's.
I didn't want to.
His house was full of dust.
Mum said I must.

Mum was often in tears.
Dad said she'd come back.
She didn't.
They didn't talk for years.

Then three years later
We all meet in a little café.
Dad talks. Mum doesn't.
But she makes Dad pay.

Then Dad goes.
Then Mum says it –
"I've never known a man before
who could grow a beard on his nose."

Split, between
two separate trees
where one tree
had been.

Saturday Dads

Up and down the High Street
With twenty grisly grins,
Go twenty grumpy Dads
With twenty prickly chins

Up and down the High Street
With twenty grouchy kids,
Twenty lots of pocket money,
That's twenty measly quids

Up and down the High Street
With twenty bags of chips,
Go twenty grumpy Dads
And twenty grisly kids

With twenty bags of chips
To fill twenty greasy tums -
Afterwards will they go home
To twenty grumpy Mums?

Snowdon By Numbers
(for Saul)

We did the first sums by the station
in Llanberis: 5 miles to the invisible Peak,
and 3000 feet, and the lonely mountain railway
not running to the summit today due to heavy cloud
and winds of up to 70 miles an hour.
You were 10 and I was 44.
You were 4' 9" and I was 6' 2".
You made a calculation and said -
"Dad, let's walk to the top."

"Oo, I'm not sure" I replied, fatherly,
and so on to other sums we discussed.
3 hours to get up there, 2 and a $\frac{1}{2}$ back down,
1 dodgy knee (mine), then 5 miles and 3000 feet
divided by 2 apples and 1 sandwich each,
the number of minutes in which storm and dark can overtake,
1 old overcoat, 1 thin anorak, no walking boots,
£3.50 for the car park. I wasn't convinced -
"Maybe $\frac{1}{2}$ way" I said "I don't promise the top."

So we set off, about $\frac{1}{2}$ past 12, slightly nervous.
You led me up by $\frac{1}{4}$'s and $\frac{1}{2}$'s and
"Just another 10 minutes, Dad, then we'll stop if you like."
Step by single step, up the long slope of the green valley,
then into fierce wet cloud, and round the elbow,
and up the steep scree, into 68 miles an hour of gale
and "We can't stop now, Dad, it's only 40 minutes",
5 feet from the end of the world, 4 legs, 2 hearts pumping,
1 final ridge, 1 summit café ahead, noone else on the track.

And at last, about 3.30, we arrive,
2 wet-through, shaking travellers. The real summit
almost invisible. So, into the cloud-wrapped café
and 70 warm, grinning summitteers in eating chaos.
At the top of the mountain that makes you feel
smaller. 2 fast cups of hot chocolate,
2 beans on toast, cake. And the pair of us
sit there grinning at each other, adding it up,
3000 feet higher, 3 hours wiser, 1 pound lighter,

maybe $\frac{1}{2}$ an inch taller.

A Good Parent

She said "Well done, love"
and "That's good" so often
she almost said it in her sleep.

"I just fell down the stairs, Mum."
"Well done, love."

"I just broke 2 fingers and my left arm, Mum."
"That's good."

"I'm off to New York for the afternoon, Mum."
"Well done, love."

"When I grow up I'm going to rob a bank."
"That's good."

"I'm thinking of giving you a bath in jelly, Mum."
"Well done."

I didn't give her a bath in jelly.
I ate the jelly instead.

(I showed my Mum this poem.
Guess what she said.)

ANGELIC

Bored with table manners?
Disappointed with not enough pocket money?
Annoyed with parents nagging?
Try …

Angelic –
the soap that gives cheeks an innocent glow

Angelic –
the soap that hides real feelings

Angelic –
the soap grown-ups love for their kids

Angelic –
The goodie-goodie way
To get through the day

THE GOODIE-GOODIE WAY

TEACHER'S PET

Tired of working hard at school?
Worried about your homework?
Fed up with never getting top marks?
Try …

Teacher's Pet -
the soap with all the answers

Teacher's Pet -
the soap for successful kids

Teacher's Pet -
the soap that fools everyone
(yes, even you)

Teacher's Pet –
Just smells like goodness

SMELLS LIKE GOODNESS

DEVIL
THE REALLY WICKED SOAP

Sick of being a goodie-goodie?
Had enough of doing what people say?
Ready for a more fun way of life?
Try …

Devil –
The soap that smells evil

Devil –
The soap that inspires the naughty you

Devil –
The really wicked soap!
The soap that puts yoghourt in your granddad's shoes!

Devil –
The really fun way
To get through the day

P.S. If you named a soap to describe what sort of person you are, what would it be called?

Three All-Purpose Excuses

1. I've been very busy giving advice to the Prime Minister
   (this child is too important to argue with)

2. I spend most of my time living in a tent on Jupiter
   (this child is too ridiculous to know how to deal with)

3. In one of my former lives I was a tiger
   (this child is slightly weird, and may be dangerous)

What are your 3 best excuses?

Write them here - if you haven't got any, make some up quickly...

1. to right !

2. so nah !

3. Keepa away

Bookworm This And Bookworm That

Said Bookworm This
To Bookworm That
"So how come you're
So squelchy fat?"

Said Bookworm That
To Bookworm This
"Well, my dear,
What I've eaten is …

Encyclopaedias, phone books,
Directories and diaries,
Grammars and primers
And whole blinking libraries

Comics, whodunits,
Harry Potter collections,
Catalogues from Ikea
And Matt Black selections

Paperbacks, palimpsests,
Atlases, histories,
Anthologies, biographies,
Manuscripts, mysteries

And there's so many more
Worm-books I eat …"
But Bookworm This
Was sound asleep -

Zzzzzzzzzzzzzzzz!

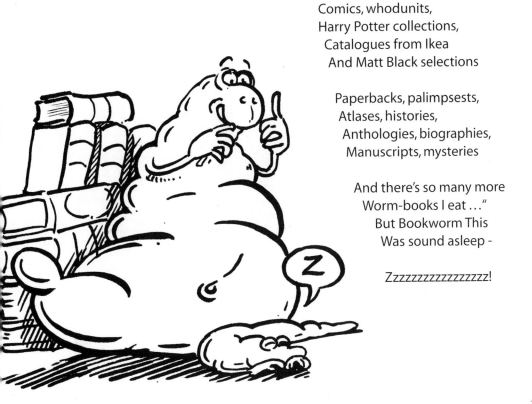

31

Porridge

There is a place called No-thoughts,
where I sometimes go,
it's quite a nice place really
when I'm tired and slow.

It's a bit like a cabbage,
or porridge or a jelly,
or the inside of a marshmallow
or a switched-off telly.

It's like a hot, summer classroom
where everyone is sleepy,
and No-ideas flop around on desks,
doing nothing, dreamy.

In this little place called No-thoughts
the teacher comes and goes,
and No-questions sink in slowly,
and noone answers, noone knows.

There is a place called No-thoughts,
where the flowers of No-thinking grow,
it's quite a nice place really
as No-thought places go.

p.s. this is a bit like Zen meditation

Just A Thought

I creep up behind you,
and I sneak right inside you,
I'm in the dark,
bad voices in your head.

I make you feel small,
I'm the shadow on the wall,
And the coldness
That creeps in your bed.

I'm the fears in your mind,
I'm cruel and unkind,
I'm the worry
That wakes you at night.

You don't know who I am?
Good, that was my plan -
I'm just a scary thought
When you turn out

The light …

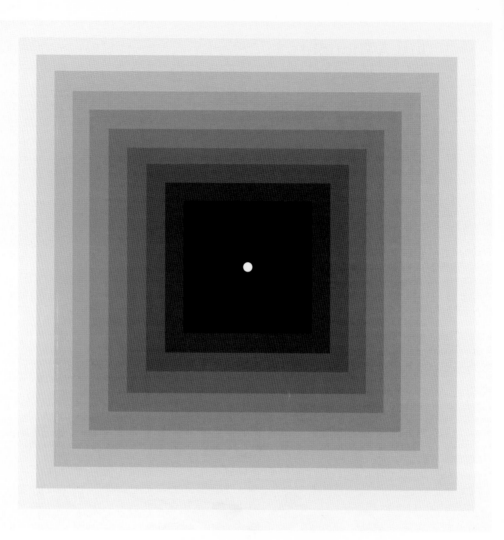

Although
destructive by
his very nature,
and feared by mortals,
the fire god is not evil
and does what he can
for mankind,
providing them
with light, warmth,
a means of cooking,
and the heat for
forging weapons
and tools.

If the
people
affront him
by neglecting
his worship, however,
he has been known
to burn cities
to the ground.

scrape of the match

scrape of the match
little red head
starting to scratch

side of the box
catch and V-oom
flower of flame
bursts into bloom

flicker of petals
yellow and red
ladybird jumping
flies from the bed

crackle and spit
flames growing claws
paper and twig
paintwork and doors

hungry animal
wanting to feed
catching and burning
branches and trees

ravage and roar
the blaze getting big
hotter than ovens
roasting a pig

eating up houses
fire in a whirl
sweeping the fields
heating the world

igniting the sun
charring the moon
hung like a lampshade
in your front room

and stars like white embers
in the black sky
watch out for sparks
hitting your eye

and always remember
a match may be small
but a fire is a dragon

in no time at all

The Boy who Loved Bonfires

His name was Bradley.
As a baby his brown eyes smouldered.
His skin was made of smoke.
As a boy he sharpened his fingers,

dipped them in phosphorous
and struck his fingertips
into little spires of fire.
He used a magnifying glass from Woolworth's

to trap the sun and set light to
little moustaches of moss
peeled from the rotting window-frames
of Uncle Steven's garage.

His mother said he was a loner.
His father said Bradley looked into the flames
and could see through red-hot time
into the white future.

Bradley was usually cheerful.
He had jokes that crackled
and he watched sunsets
with a smile.

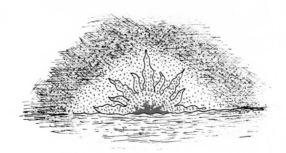

Later he fell in love with a woman called Jane
who painted her toenails red
and when she laughed
the air burst into yellow.

They got married
standing in a large pile
of autumn leaves,
like rusty confetti.

The wedding feast
was soup and jacket potatoes.
Now he is forty two
and working happily

in the Italian pizza restaurant
in the town centre
feeding suns of dough
into the oven.

Wild

Isn't water great? I mean, clouds - aren't they brilliant?
Looking like ducks, crocodiles, dogs. Brilliant, in' it.
And spaghetti rivers. Wicked. And snow -
Isn't that magic? Big fairy snowflakes, then curvy icing
like bobsleigh runs over hedges and rooves,
moon houses and Christmas cake streets. And icicles -
aren't they wicked! dripping like long noses with a cold.
And scary mist, and big black lakes, where monsters prowl.

And warm rivers for swimming in. Brilliant. Yea, but wait -
the best is still to come. O yes, the sea. Fantastic.
Timeless. Raw power. What can beat that?
Cool. And mighty. Always changing its feelings.
Still. Then roaring. Try to get your head round that.
It's like trying to paint your life. Brilliant.

Win
ter
Rid
dle

Soft
as
feathers,

cool as
drops
of milk,

in flurries
fluttering
like

dancing
circles of
silk,

like drifting
confetti of
white   lace,

I'm a soft
veil of
winter -

floating
over
your
face

Seven Questions to the Lighthouse Keeper

O tell me please, Peter, Peter,
How you became the lighthouse keeper?
  In bed, with my bike-light flashing off and on,
  When I was all at sea, when I was young.

O tell me please, Peter, Peter,
Who talks to you, the lighthouse keeper?
  O the waves they chatter, fish sing the blues
  And the west wind brings the morning news.

O tell me please, Peter, Peter,
Who can be a lighthouse keeper?
  Why, dreamers and loners and people like me
  With their heads in the clouds and their souls in the sea.

O tell me please, Peter, Peter,
What makes you smile, lighthouse keeper?
  When the light is flashing, and the moon up high,
  And I disco all night in my room in the sky.

O tell me please, Peter, Peter,
Aren't you sad being the lighthouse keeper?
  Why, looking out for others keeps me warm
  And I am safe in the eye of the storm.

O tell me please, Peter, Peter,
What's best about being the lighthouse keeper?
  Ah, eating toast and sipping tea
  And watching the sun fall into the sea.

O tell me please, Peter, Peter,
What can I bring you, lighthouse keeper?
  Well, maybe just a small locket of land,
  And a wife, a cat and a watering can.

Love-Monster

Haircut boys
Smoochy lips
Lipstick girls
Kiss-me-quicks

   Do the Monster, do the Monster,
   Do the Monster Love

Jill loves Jim
Jim loves Jane
The Love-Monster
Is back again

   Do the Monster, do the Monster,
   Do the Monster Love

With big green wings
You are next
Bus stop dates
Text, text, text

   Do the Monster, do the Monster,
   Do the Monster Love

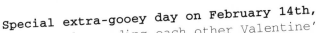

Special extra-gooey day on February 14th, with people sending each other Valentine's chocolates, flowers, cards. Started in Rome of course. Many daft traditions, including: if you cut an apple in half and count how many seeds are inside, you will know how many children you will have.

I recommend: wearing dark glasses or staying at home.

Valentine's Day
Pink and blue
Yukety yuk
Goo double goo

Do the Monster, do the Monster,
Do the Monster Love

No escape
Nothing to do
The Love-Monster
Will get to you

The loony Monster
The swoony Monster
The beautiful, beautiful Moony Monster -
Love!

there's a goblin in the fridge
there's a goblin in the fridge

he's got big green eyes that stare
and a head of wiry hair
but he's the goblin noone sees
because he hides behind the cheese

and if you look behind the cheese
he quickly slips behind the peas
and if you ask him "Are you real?"
the goblin cries "I'll make a deal –

if you'll believe in me
then I'll believe in you"
which is clever don't you see
because you want it to be true

and so you look behind the peas
but he slips inside the freezer
and once inside the freezer
he's the goblin you will never, never, never, never find

but then you'll sometimes hear
his quiet laugh – ha ha ha ha ha
because he's a little teaser
the secret goblin in your mind

the secret goblin in the fridge
this little goblin geezer

Song of the Golden Dimorphodon

Here I am,
golden Dimorphodon!
They call me
the glowing one.

My leathery wings
creased like old brown paper.
My enormous beak
like a gold mountain.

With my big eyes,
like spinning suns,
I see into the ancient, boggy past,
look into the unknown future.

insects

I eat tiny fish and insects,
gobbling them down
the crinkly crater
of my mouth.

One day I shall be
king of Devon,
wearing an invisible crown
on my strange birdish head.

For now I just hang on
to the rough bark
of the present,
counting a million years.

tiny fish

has anyone seen an invisible crown?

The Grumpy Unicorn

I didn't exactly choose it, did I,
with this long, thin ice-cream cornet
plopped in the middle of my forehead.

People think it's easy, this game,
look cool, be all kind of mythical,
but like everyone, I've had my struggles.

Even at school, stupid things happened -
I couldn't do forward rolls in P.E., kids teased me,
they used my horn as a toilet-roll holder.

I mean, you try putting on a t-shirt over this.
Or getting re-housed down at the council
when nobody believes you are real.

See what I mean, you don't know the half of it -
how do you think I find a bicycle helmet?
And people stare at me in the swimming pool.

And girlfriends. Do you think it's easy
Finding someone when you look this different?
No, I'm not different, or special, to me I'm normal.

I don't want a lot - just not to be stared at
like I come from another country, or universe;
and to be talked to like you believe I really exist.

And of course I don't want to end up in some fairground
near those horses, with a job as some joke-creature,
like a prong for doughnuts or a game of hoopla.

dot-2-dot or star-2-star

This is the constellation called Monoceros, one of the night sky's own dot-to-dot puzzles. Join up the stars and see what it becomes.

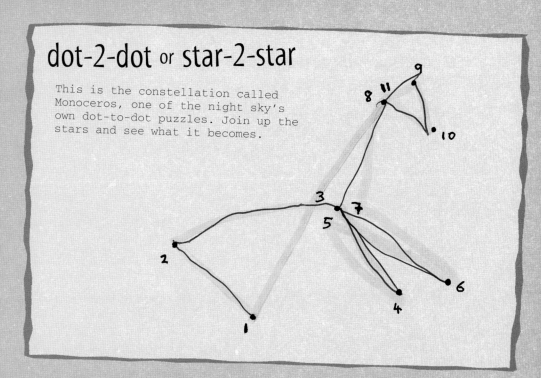

did you know?
some unicorn facts

The Unicorn is one of the most mysterious of all animals. It has not been seen for centuries, and some people say it can only be seen by those of exceptional virtue and honesty.

One of the first unicorns is said to have appeared in China almost 5,000 years ago to give Emperor Fu Hsi the secrets of written language.

In the third century B.C. Alexander the Great boasted that he rode a unicorn into battle.

My postman Brian is a unicorn, but not everybody knows this.

Dear Problem Page,

I don't know what to do. I'm nearly fifteen and my friends keep laughing at me and saying that I'm not going to get a girlfriend. See, the thing is I feel a bit different to most people. I know I've just got to be myself, but I am a bit different. I've got this ice-cream cornet in the middle of my forehead and when I go shopping . . . .

49

When Is A Banana
Not A Banana?

I am a banana,
said the banana.
Actually, this is a joke.
I am not a banana -
for as you know, bananas can't speak.
So, this is a poem
and I am a word-banana
pretending to be a real-banana.
This is not a joke.
Actually, I am not a word-banana,
I am a person, talking to you,
pretending to be a banana.
Why?
Because last night I cried
and I felt like a banana.
Do bananas cry? Don't ask.
This is too confusing.

Am I a person
pretending to be a banana?

Or am I a banana
pretending to be a person?

Or am I a lemon?

When If A Banana Not A Banana?

I am a banana,
said the bandana.
Actually, this is a joke.
I am not a banana -
for as you know, bananas can't squeak.
So, this is a pom
and I am a word-banana
pretending to be a meal-banana.
This is not a joke.
Actually I am not a bird-banana,
I am a person, walking to you,
pretending to be a banana.
Why?
Because last night I fried
and I smelt like a fried banana.
Do bananas fry? Don't ask.
This is too confusing.

Am I a person
Pretending to be a banana?

Or am I a banana
Pretending to be a parson?

Or ham I a lemon?

There are **14 differences** between this poem and the poem on the left hand side. **Can you spot them?**

Why?

Why do swallows fly in patterns like synchronised swimmers?
Why do pampered poodles look like their owners?
Why does water swirl around the plughole?
Why do my legs go jumpy with rock 'n roll?
Why am I who I am? Why are you you?
Why is the sky blue?

Why do peacocks' feathers have eyes like rainbows?
Why do people say "That's just how it goes"?
Why was I born in England, not Africa, or Iceland?
Why do clouds look like giant sheep or mountains?
Why am I who I am? Why are you you?
Why is the sky blue?

Why do butchers look so pink and jolly?
Why do parrots get called Polly?
Why do pears look like giant teardrops?
Why do tears look like tiny peardrops?
Why am I who I am? Why are you you?
Why is the sky blue?

Why was I not born as a spider, or a sloth?
Why does chocolate melt like music in the mouth?
Why do oak leaves have veins like rivers?
Why do sycamore seeds spin like helicopters?
Why am I who I am? Why are you you?
Why is the sky true?

Why do some poems
ask so many questions ...?

Why? Why? Why?

WHY NOT HAVE A GO AT YOUR OWN WHY POEM?

How can you write your own poem like this? I started by brainstorming all the Why? questions I could think of. You can use Why? questions for how things work, people in jobs, animals, plants, things in the home, inventions, holidays, food, behaviour, grown-ups, kids - whatever you like. My list was 3 or 4 times the number that I ended up with. I then selected the best ones, and the ones that went together well in pairs, numbering them first, then writing and juggling them round on new sheets of paper.

Notice:

- the lines are in pairs, and some of the pairs rhyme

- when they don't rhyme the pairs usually have a similar sound at the end of the line

- I used a couple of my favourite pairs for the first two lines of the first verse, and the last two lines of the last verse

- I have put lines together with similar ideas or sounds - oak leaves go with sycamore seeds, peacocks starts with the same sound as people

- it's not themed all the way through - that might be too obvious

- there is no set length for a line here, though pairs of lines usually have similiar lengths to help the rhythm

FINALLY, you don't have to have a chorus. And it doesn't have to rhyme. And it could easily be much shorter. Two verses of four lines would be fine - and actually might be better than this, which is a bit long, but I can't resist it.

Have fun!

The Argument

He just came at me, know what I mean?
His fists rippling, pink knucklebones,
raw and tight, but blurred too,
I didn't really see them, I was too busy
watching the red heat in his eyes -
"Sorry" I shouted "please, I didn't mean to"
and there was another blur of fingers
and his voice roaring through like a train –

"You touch my brother again ..."
and he grabbed my shirt, top button came off,
crunched me up against the wall,
I saw the red flecks in his eyes burning, like I'd
touched him, hurt him. I was scared.
I put my hand on the round bone of his shoulder
and did my look-him-in-the-eye thing,

"Sorry" I said, and his eyes cooled a bit,
his shoulders dropped an inch, his fists unclenched,
and he half-turned away - "Alright" he said,
"just don't do it again." And off he went,
his hands swinging by his side like soft gloves,
and he left me there, my heart pumping like a rabbit,
my eyes watering, and fresh with the cold.

Thank You, Jack

When Claire said
"Jack's crying, Miss",
it was like a gust of wind
rustled the class.

Most of us looked.
We knew this feeling ourselves.
Too much, suddenly too much
rushing at us too fast.

"Thank you, Jack" said Miss,
who had once told us that tears
were like beautiful leaves
falling on grass.

Some turned their heads away.
Others watched Jack
as he cried on his own
till the wind blew past.

The Language of Worms

Best done at night
when the world is asleep,
put your ear to the earth
and hear down in the deep -

schlewbaar
gr-r-r-r-r-r-r-ewba
oooompa-pa-pa-pa-paaaa
ssschl-l-l-l-l-l-l-l-l-luuuurr!!!

6 shy haikus found hiding in the oaks in Parkin Woods

twisting antler world -
dancing branches, swirling leaves
reaching for the sun

small village of ants
who carry moss, twigs, busy
paths lit by bluebells

alligator log
just lies there, green eyes watching,
waiting for dinner

midnight, silver bark
like strange white faces sleeping,
quiet moons lost in love

curvy branch like snake
slithers under dark green bush -
my mind disappears

in deep damp brown mud
worms play loud wiggle 'n roll -
worm palace disco

Eight Questions in Parkin Woods

What do you hear,
dirty brown track?
   The giggling toes of children
   dance on my back

What do you hear,
whispering leaves?
   The swirl of voices
   caroodle through trees

What do you hear,
big, brown log?
   The creakee croakee
   of a fat green frog

What do you hear,
yellow biscuit of sun?
   The world's trees breathe
   and sigh as one

What do you hear,
snaky darkness of roots?
   Granny Centipedes knitting
   hundreds of boots

What do you hear,
owl with the moonface?
  Mice and silver wings
  swooping through space

What do you hear,
tall and mighty tree?
  The far distant prayer
  of the roar of the sea

What do you hear,
bendy branches up high?
  The squeaky wheelbarrow bird
  Sings through the sky

The Millipede Rap

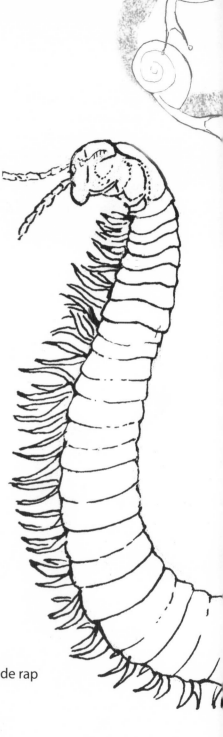

Tap tap, tap tap, tap tap, tap tap,
Tap tap, tap tap, tap tap, tap tap,
Tap tap, tap tap, tap tap, tap tap,
Tip tap, tip tap, tap tap, tap tap

Do the tippety tap, tip tap, tip tap,
Do the milli, do the milli,
Do the millipede rap

Tap tap, tip tip, tap tap, tap tap,
Tap tap, tippety, tippety, tap,
Tap tap, tip tap, tap tap, tap tap,
Tippety, tippety, tippety tap

Do the tippety tap, tip tap, tip tap,
Do the milli, do the milli,
Do the millipede rap

Tippety, tippety, tippety, tap
Tappety, toppety, tuppety, tip
Tippety, toppety, tappety, tap

Do the silly, do the milli,
Do the millipede rap

Footnote!
this is ten times better than the centipede rap

The Snail Rap

Munch munch,
  munch munch,
    munch munch,
  munch munch,

  munch munch,
  munch
CRUNCH!

O dear, what was that?

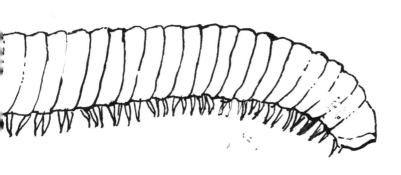

Goblin In The Fridge Quiz

Here are 10 questions linked to the poems in the book.
Send a set of good answers to quizzes@matt-black.co.uk
and you will receive a mystery prize poem.

1. Which word in the poem 'Alphabetti Spaghetti' did he think
he'd made up but was actually in the dictionary? What does it mean?

2. What creatures are claimed to sometimes hide in watering-cans?
Do you think this is true? Where else might you find these creatures
hidden in this book? Have you ever seen one?

3. What song does 'Lord of the Doughnuts' remind you of?
What other creation myths do you know?

4. If you count up all the twenties in 'Saturday Dads', how many are
there? Do you think Dads are generally grumpier than Mums?

5. Which poem is the word 'palimpsest' in? Do you know what it means?
Have you ever made one with a pencil and rubber?

6. What makes Peter the lighthouse keeper smile?
Have you ever seen a lighthouse? What do you remember about it?

7. What did the children at the grumpy unicorn's school use his horn
for?

8. What is your favourite line in the 'Why?' poem?
Why is it your favourite line?

9. Which kind of music do worms play in Parkin Woods?

10. Write 3 nonsense words beginning with A, B and C to start your own
nonsense alphabet poem (like 'Alphabotsie, Alphaboodle').

Goblin In The Fridge Wordsearch

Find at least one word from each poem in the book. That makes 46 words – and there are a few extra words as well. They can be found horizontally, vertically, diagonally and from left to right or right to left. If you need help the story below includes the words (alphabetically) that come from the poems.

```
L N D N I K N U S I L L Y P R
G P Q O E C A L R K P I N K U
Q B O G T A L P S A D N E S S
G M U D D L E O R C U K M U T
O H D C S B I R D I S H N G L
R M N R T T O R Y B T S O A E
F O I A E T Z I T F H G B R B
A O W C S A N D W I C H L Y N
P N O K N M M G N O G A R D F
T T G L U E U E A B B E A R D
H E P E S W M S R S T B R J Q
R E N E L B B U B S L Q L S R
X T E T W I G S N I G H T Y M
X H S P I H C O V C J O K E C
C F J P A R M E W B H F D U M
```

It was an angelic bank, run by a man with a beard. A birdish woman, inside a bubble, eating cheese and chips which crackled, walked in with 2 dogs and a dragon. "Is this a place for dreamers?" she asked the manager. "Oh no" he said. "it is a place of dust for evil fools and frogs." And he blew a horn. This was not a joke. The woman wore lace, and behind her glided in MattBlack, like a monster, still mooing at the moon and with mud around his heels. "This is a muddle," he said, "I've been out there, munching all night, with parrots, bowls of pink porridge. I wrote a rap, I heard a rustle, and there was sadness in my sandwich." "You're silly," said the manager. "Splat!" said Matt, "here's some sugary sums for you – 2 sunsets minus sunshine equals what? And what do you get if you put fifty teeth in a tent with eleven tigers and a bunch of twigs?" "Don't be unkind." said the wind, blowing in through the bank door. It was a wobbly day.

Shortest Riddle In The World

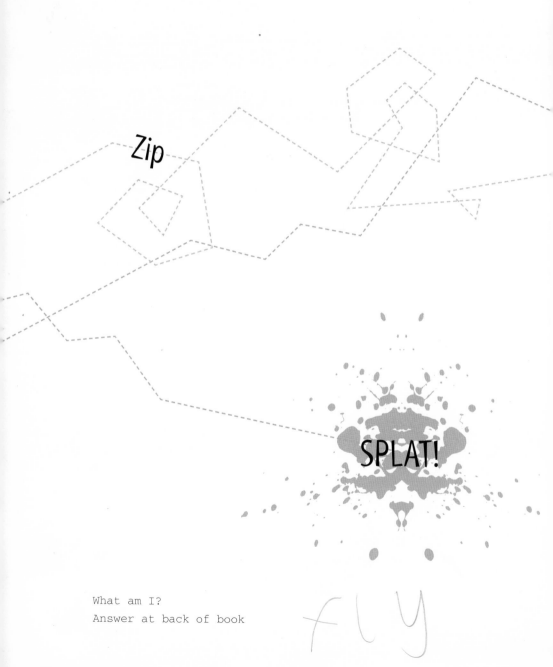

Zip

SPLAT!

What am I?
Answer at back of book

fly

Fastest Riddle In The World
(to be read very fast, with only one breath per verse)

In the middle of the muddle of the sandwich of this riddle
when your mind is lost in battle and your ears begin to wriggle
and you're in a bit of trouble and you're getting in a piggle
and you're starting to unravel and you wobble in this puzzle

then your thoughts begin to huddle and an idea starts to juggle
of the final fickle answer that'll travel from the riddle
and you squiggle and you giggle and your eyes go round and wiggle
there's a niggle and a tickle and your legs begin to jiggle

when you realise it's so simple and the way that it begins'll
unriddle now the muddle of the struggle of the straggle
of the scrabble babble gabble the edible digestible
in the middle of the sandwich cos the answer's cheese and …

Answer at back of book.

Elghant

O dear, one line is missing a syllable . . .
Which one?

You Smell Like My Dad

Burger and fries,
After-shave in a mist,
Armpits and moonshine,
Friendship and crisps.

Jumper and doughnuts,
Five pints of beer,
Loneliness and vinegar,
Quick whiff of fear.

Bristles and garlic,
Lemon and zest,
Honey and lies,
Parfum de vest.

Sawdust and soap,
River and strife,
Petrol and laughter,
Seaweed and life.

Old socks and sadness,
New car and wet dog,
Shouting and woodsmoke,
Fried onions and love.

Not As Young As He Used To Be

asleep in armchair,
cave-mouth, no teeth, dream-whistles
favourite old tunes

The Granny Power Rap

One fine day in the middle of a nap
A little voice said "You gotta write a rap"
Rap - that's cool - but I ain't no youth
So I better write a rap with my own kind of truth

Click clack click clack crackety crick
Do the Dodgy Shoulder, Do the Dodgy Hip
Click clack click clack crickety crack
You ain't gonna stop the Old Geezers Rap -
Cos when we feel good, we shout "Hwaaaa!
You ain't gonna stop - GRANNY POWER!"

So I tap me rap, aged forty-seven,
Sweet little age, close to heaven,
But inside - yea - still a young child -
Feeling frisky, risky, wicked and wild
And guess what, kids, it's fun over here
In my carpet slippers with a bottle of beer,
Ballroom dancing, foxtrot, tango
Home for telly and a nice cup of cocoa

Click clack click clack creekity cree
Do the Cup of Cocoa Do the Cup of Tea
Click clack click clack crickity crack
You ain't gonna stop the Old Geezers Rap
Cos when we feel good, we shout "Hwaaaa!
You ain't gonna stop - GRANNY POWER!"

When I run upstairs, I run out of breath
And at the top, there stands De-e-e-e-eath
But Death just says "You're too soon, babeeeeeee,
Come back later" and I say "Maybeeee"
Cos I'm too busy doing the stick - doing the hat -
Fighting fit, fighting fat, dodgy hip, dodgy back
But when we feel good, we shout "Hwaaaa!
You ain't gonna stop GRANNY POWER!"

Alphabotsie, Alphaboodle

Archer-varcher
Booga
Chrimble
Doo-dah-day

Eggy-peggy
Fobble
Gabbly-gub
Hoo-ha-hey

Iggly-jiggly
Joo-joo-jam
Karamba
Limpopo
Moo

Nobbly
Obbly
Pipsidissimus
Quiggly
Riggly
Stroggly
Too

Umpop
Veega
Woggle-woggle

Xmiff
Yogo
Zoohoohoo

Why not have a go at making up
your own nonsense alphabet?

Arch-Fart   Liky   soogey
bocaJ   moot
Chicky   Nibbly
doo-doo-das   ogg
Exy-mexy   Pipey
Fibble   Quack
Gooby-Goo   rig
Hoot-ne-hey   Strag
iggy-pigy   tock
loo-to   Joo-Joo-Joo
Kooby   wigle-wigle um vac xmas yogs

—Quousque tandem
abutere, Catilina
patientia nostra
nos etiam

Riddle answers

Where The Wild Wind p. 13:
The Planet Earth

Wriggly Riddly p. 16:
Jelly

Shortest Riddle In The World p.64:
A fly banging into a window

Fastest Riddle In The World p.65:
Elephant

Wordsearch answers

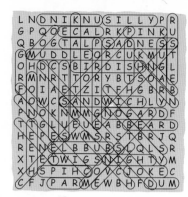

A brief history of jelly p. 16:

Jelly
has been
eaten since
Egyptian times.
The first concentrated
Jelly cube arrived in 1932.

Footnotes to 'Pizza Pizza' p.17

Pizza Margherita was named after Queen Margherita di Savoia, Queen of Italy, who chose it in 1889 as her favourite pizza. It was made by the most famous pizza maker in Italy at that time, Raffaele Esposito.

Pizza has been part of the Italian diet since the Stone Age. One of the good things about pizza is that it uses bread as an edible plate. Evidence of pizzas was found in the ashes of Pompeii after Mount Vesuvius erupted – these were called Pizza Burnti.

For further copies or to contact Matt Black:
email: info@matt-black.co.uk
Upside Down Books, 51 Pearson Place, Sheffield S8 9DE